How to use this book

Follow the advice, in italics, given for you on each page.
Support the children as they read the text that is shaded in cream.
Praise *the children at every step!*

Detailed guidance is provided in the Read Write Inc. Phonics Handbook

9 reading activities

Children:
Practise reading the speed sounds.
Read the green, red and challenge words for the story.
Listen as you read the introduction.
Discuss the vocabulary check with you.
Read the story.
Re-read the story and discuss the 'questions to talk about'.
Read the story with fluency and expression.
Answer the questions to 'read and answer'.
Practise reading the speed words.

Speed sounds

Consonants *Say the pure sounds (do not add 'uh').*

f ff	l ll le	m mm	n nn (kn)	r rr	s ss (se) (ce)	v ve	z zz s	sh	th	ng nk

b bb	c k ck	d dd	g gg	h	j	p pp	qu	t tt	w wh	x	y	ch tch

Vowels *Say the sounds in and out of order.*

at	hen head	in	on	up	day	see happy he	high find	blow no

zoo	look	car	for door snore	fair	whirl	shout	boy spoil

*Each box contains one sound but sometimes more than one grapheme. Focus graphemes are **circled**.*

Green words

str<u>ee</u>t   s<u>or</u>t   fl<u>oor</u>   <u>ar</u>m   gr<u>ee</u>n

<u>ou</u>t   sn<u>ou</u>t   m<u>ou</u><u>th</u>   pr<u>ou</u>d   h<u>ou</u><u>se</u>   r<u>ou</u>nd   c<u>ou</u>nt   gr<u>ou</u>nd   l<u>ou</u>d   f<u>ou</u>nd

c<u>ou</u><u>ch</u>   s<u>ou</u>nd   p<u>ou</u>nd   <u>ou</u><u>ch</u>   <u>sh</u><u>ou</u>t   <u>our</u>   b<u>ou</u>nce   p<u>ou</u>nce

Read in syllables.

g<u>ar</u>` den → g<u>ar</u>den          al` w<u>ays</u> → alw<u>ays</u>

f<u>or</u>` get → f<u>or</u>get          pl<u>ay</u>` ground → pl<u>ay</u>gr<u>ou</u>nd

a` b<u>ou</u>t → ab<u>ou</u>t          ki<u>ck</u>` a` b<u>ou</u>t → ki<u>ck</u>ab<u>ou</u>t

kno<u>ck</u>` <u>ou</u>t → kno<u>ck</u> <u>ou</u>t          B<u>ou</u>nd` <u>er</u> → B<u>ou</u>nd<u>er</u>

Read the root word first and then with the ending.

b<u>ou</u>nce → b<u>ou</u>ncy   p<u>ou</u>nce → p<u>ou</u>nced

dev<u>our</u> → dev<u>our</u>ed   gr<u>ou</u><u>ch</u> → gr<u>ou</u><u>ch</u>y

Red words

anyo<u>ne</u>   <u>o</u>v<u>er</u>   <u>who</u>   a<u>ll</u>   <u>o</u><u>ne</u>   wa<u>tch</u>

d<u>oe</u>s   <u>they</u>   s<u>ch</u><u>oo</u>l

Challenge words

<u>g</u>u<u>ess</u>   wa<u>sh</u> er   gr<u>ey</u><u>h</u>ound   d<u>ou</u><u>b</u>t

Our house

Introduction

Describe your house – who lives there?
What's the best thing about it?
This story describes a boy's house. We don't get to know
his name but he tells us all about his home and family.
When stories are written like this we call the character
telling the story the narrator.

Although his house is messy and a bit chaotic at times
I think he rather likes his home and his family.

Story written by Gill Munton
Illustrated by Tim Archbold

Vocabulary check

Discuss the meaning (as used in the story) after the children have read each word.

	definition:	sentence/phrase:
doubt	don't think so	I doubt if you'd bother to stop next to it.
pound	hurt	Carl plays his CD's so loud my head starts to pound.
grouchy	grumpy	Mum can get a bit grouchy.
couch	sofa	We have our dinner on the couch.
pounced	jumped	He pounced on it...
devoured	ate really quickly	...and devoured it at top speed.
snout	dog's nose	Bounder stuck his snout into my hand.
knockout	really good	He's a knockout at football.

Punctuation to note in this story:
1. Capital letters to start sentences and full stop to end sentences
2. Capital letters for names
3. Exclamation marks to show anger, shock and surprise
4. 'Wait and see' dots...
5. Apostrophe to show contractions: doesn't they're we're

Our house

Our house isn't much to look at.

I doubt if you'd bother to stop next to it

if you went along Mount Street (that's our street).

Not that anyone much goes along Mount Street.

(It's that kind of street.)

Our house is sort of pink, with a red door and a little

garden all round it. I can't begin to count the weeds in that garden.

And Bounder (Grandad's greyhound), is always digging

up the ground, looking for his bouncy ball.

We've got three bedrooms – one for Mum, one
for Grandad (and Bounder) and one for me and Carl.
Carl plays his CDs for hours, so loud that – ouch!
- my head starts to pound.

Then Mum shouts up the stairs and says "Stop that!".
(She can get a bit grouchy, our Mum.)

Most days we have our dinner on the couch, watching TV.
Last week, Bounder found a bit of
egg sandwich next to Grandad's chair.

He pounced on it and
devoured it at top speed.

Yuck.

We've just got one small bathroom.

So when Bounder's having his bath,

you can forget about going to the loo

or washing your hands

for about ten hours.

Grandad gets shampoo and

dog hairs all over the floor –

and guess who gets to mop it up!

I'm in bed as I'm telling you all this.
I was just thinking – it doesn't sound much,
our house. But it's not that bad.
Tonight, Mum sent me to the corner shop
to get some flour and I got a pound,
for sweets. They were so good, I stuffed
about six into my mouth.

When I got back, Bounder stuck his snout into my hand and
started to lick my arm. They're fantastic dogs, greyhounds, and so fast!
Bounder can run at about 60 km an hour.

Then Carl and I went out to Southways Park to have a kickabout in the playground. He's a knockout at football, our Carl.

He plays for our school. I guess I'm proud of him.

And when I went to bed,
Grandad chatted to me as
I brushed my teeth.

Then he said, was I too old for a story.

I said no, I wasn't.

Our house is ...

... too small

... full of shouting

... a bit of a mess (well, some days).

But it's never boring.

Our house is – well, it's all right.

Questions to talk about

Re-read the page. Read the question to the children. Tell them whether it is a **FIND IT** *question or* **PROVE IT** *question.*

FIND IT ·

✓ *Turn to the page*

✓ *Read the question*

✓ *Find the answer*

PROVE IT

✓ *Turn to the page*

✓ *Read the question*

✓ *Find your evidence*

✓ *Explain why*

Page 9:	PROVE IT	*Why does the narrator says that he 'doubts people would bother to stop'? What's your first impression of the house?*
Page 10:	PROVE IT	*What does he feel about sharing a bedroom with Carl?*
Page 11:	PROVE IT	*What does Bounder think about the family eating their dinner on the couch?*
Page 12:	FIND IT	*What happens when Grandad is bathing Bounder?*
Page 13:	PROVE IT	*I think the narrator wants us to know he quite likes his house. Which sentence tells us this? Do you think he likes Bounder?*
Page 14:	FIND IT	*Why is the narrator proud of Carl? What did Grandad ask Carl?*
Page 15:	PROVE IT	*What does the narrator really like about his house?*

Questions to read and answer

(Children complete without your help.)

1. What does the house look like? The house has...

2. Why is Mum grouchy? She is grouchy because...

3. What happens when Bounder has a bath? When Bounder has a bath...

4. What is Carl good at? Carl is good at ...

5. Why is your house a good house? It is good because...

Speed words

Children practise reading the words across the rows, down the columns and in and out of order clearly and quickly.

green	always	school	bedrooms	stairs
forget	found	playground	hour	shout
round	loud	watching	anyone	goes
most	down	aren't	can't	like